the international art fair for contemporary objects

presented by the crafts council

14—17 may 2010

saatchi gallery
duke of york's hq
chelsea london

COLLECT: the international art fair for contemporary objects is presented by the Crafts Council

Crafts Council
44a Pentonville Road
London N1 9BY, UK
T +44 (0) 20 7278 7700
www.craftscouncil.org.uk
Registered Charity No. 280956
ISBN-10 1903713218
ISBN-13 9781903713211

With thanks to the selection panel
Thimo te Duits, *Conservator Design; Design Curator, Museum Boijmans Van Beuningen*
Alun Graves, *Curator in the department of sculpture, metalwork, ceramics and glass, V&A Museum*
Ben Williams, *Contemporary ceramics specialist, Phillips de Pury*

Graphic Design
John Morgan studio

Logistics Management
20–20 Events Management Ltd

Stand Construction
Stabilo International

Official Shipper
Williams & Hill Forwarding Ltd

PR Agency
Calum Sutton

The Crafts Council is supported by Arts Council England. Arts Council England works to get great art to everyone by championing, developing and investing in artistic experiences that enrich people's lives. As the national development agency for the arts, it supports a range of artistic activities from theatre to music, literature to dance, photography to digital art, and carnival to crafts. Between 2008 and 2011, Arts Council England will invest £1.3 billion of public money from government and a further £0.3 billion from the National Lottery to create these experiences for as many people as possible across the country.

Additional thanks to
Saatchi Gallery
Own Art

Supported by
ARTS COUNCIL ENGLAND

Contents

We are delighted to welcome you to the seventh COLLECT. Because last year was such a success, the fair has been extended to run over four days and, as with last year, offers an unparalleled mixture of international and national work from across the spectrum of craft practice. This year the spectrum expands still further, ranging from iconic work by Lucie Rie and Hans Coper, presented by first time exhibitor Galerie Besson, to work created in 2010 specifically for COLLECT and the impressive Saatchi Gallery space.

Each year many returning galleries introduce us to new and exciting artists from their countries, ensuring that COLLECT remains at the forefront of the contemporary craft market. Work continues to be made that has something new to say and new ways to say it, thus demonstrating the expansive creative vocabulary at makers' fingertips. This year is no different, with many galleries presenting their artists in increasingly innovative and ambitious ways. Dovecot Studio is one such gallery. It will present a solo installation by artist Claire Barclay and the Dovecot master weavers. It is spirit-lifting to see how vibrant and indeed vital the sector remains despite the difficult recent times of the last decade.

COLLECT would not be possible without the combined efforts of many people. Our thanks go to Arts Council England for its continued support, the Saatchi Gallery for such a marvellous venue, all the Crafts Council staff and most importantly the galleries and the hundreds of exhibiting artists whose creativity and dedication continues to inspire us all, and to make COLLECT one of the most enjoyable dates on the cultural calendar.

I hope you enjoy this catalogue, and that it will be a trusted guide as well as a beautiful reminder of the objects that we are collecting at the start of a new decade.

Joanna Foster CBE, Chair, Crafts Council

We were thrilled with the success of last year's COLLECT at the Saatchi Gallery – a venue befitting the exceptional contemporary craft exhibited there. The dour financial climate didn't dampen the collecting spirit, and it is with continued optimism that we approach COLLECT 2010. Once more this is a thoroughly international affair with galleries from 14 countries representing 419 makers, 70% based outside the UK. Curators from across the UK will again be given the chance to acquire this world-class contemporary craft through the Art Fund COLLECT scheme, which will have contributed £200,000 to the acquisition of craft by public collections after this year's fair.

Craft makes a large contribution to the financial success of the Creative Industries; in total £3 billion to the UK economy each year, greater for example than that made by the Cultural Heritage and Literature sectors.

This is a significant contribution to a world-respected creative economy and it is down to the creativity and commitment to quality and innovation of British makers. Craft is very much rooted in material, but its process increasingly uses CAD, rapid prototyping and other digital technologies. There are many beneficial interfaces between making and the digital and new media industries, but we must be mindful that the creative industries do not become exclusively defined in such terms. The furthering of innovative work with real materials and real physical processes will always be essential to the creative and knowledge economy of the future.

Importantly COLLECT offers work that embraces new technologies alongside work that celebrates the centuries-old alchemy which happens when material and process are connected by the skill of the hand. We will see this in abundance within the fair and also along the COLLECT Trail; a series of showcases throughout Kensington and Chelsea including the nearby TASCHEN store, Designers Guild and Duke of York Square, where six emerging makers will showcase new work that focuses on the hand in craft.

COLLECT presents such a variety of work that it is hard to believe that anyone would visit without desiring at least one item. So enjoy this opportunity to see, learn and collect some of the very best contemporary craft that is being made in the world today.

Rosy Greenlees, Executive Director, Crafts Council

The Art Fund and Collect

Art Fund COLLECT was launched by The Art Fund and the Crafts Council in 2008, championing contemporary craft and increasing its presence in UK collections. A funding pot of £50,000 was to be offered to selected curators across the country, to allow them to select and purchase outright a unique work from the Crafts Council's international fair, COLLECT.

Since 2005 The Art Fund has encouraged curators to apply – via its established grants system – for funding for acquisitions from COLLECT. Art Fund COLLECT is specifically tailored to the fair itself, offering 100% grants to winners. In its initial call for entries, The Art Fund invited all UK curators with contemporary craft collections, or collections they felt would be enriched through an acquisition from COLLECT, to apply. From the start, the judging committee has embraced applications that demonstrate an appreciation for the international remit of COLLECT, as well as a clear curatorial vision. Curators are asked in their applications to specify their museum or gallery's specific collecting ambitions – that is, which galleries and makers they are interested in, and why. In 2008, we received 23 applications and short-listed ten. Last year, of (once again) 23 applications, seven new venues applied to take part, with 16 returning from the previous year. We short-listed ten and five were successful.

Because of the speedy decision-making process, with winners announced on the day itself, and the provision of 100% grants towards each winning piece, the scheme is incontrovertibly an effective and imaginative way of immediately boosting public collections with contemporary craft. Since 2009, we have allocated £75,000 for Art Fund COLLECT – and this has bought such works as an impressive, large-scale vase by Julian Stair to MIMA (Middlesbrough Institute of Modern Art), an intricately crafted silver piece by Junko Mori to the Ulster Museum and much else besides.

Art Fund COLLECT has certainly had an impact, sparking an astonishing 70% increase in successful applications to The Art Fund for contemporary craft. Since 2008, we have awarded a total of 29 grants towards international craft pieces, including the nine final prizes at Art Fund COLLECT in 2008 and 2009, as well as a further eight granted towards works spotted at the fair by applicants who did not go on to win on the day. To put this in perspective, we awarded a total of 17 grants towards contemporary craft in the preceding two years.

The curator of craft at MIMA, James Beighton, has won a piece at Art Fund COLLECT for two years running and believes that the scheme helps nurture astute curatorial choices. 'I very much admire the principles of Art Fund COLLECT. The trust offered to curatorial judgement is most welcome, and I feel sets a helpful precedent. The application process helped to focus curatorial attention on the importance of craft to their venue and the role that it can play in their exhibition policy. I also feel that it was helpful to nudge curators into doing more advance research about COLLECT.'

Art Fund COLLECT is also a social occasion. The scheme offers a wonderful opportunity for curators of craft to come together and exchange ideas, before the competition itself and at the Private View afterwards, to which all applicants are invited. Kate Gillespie, Assistant Keeper of Applied Art from Aberdeen Art Gallery, was among last year's winners, and is enthusiastic: 'It presented an unparalleled opportunity to gain experience and knowledge of current makers working in the UK and abroad... In addition I was keen to meet the other participating museum and gallery professionals who also work with contemporary craft.'

The Art Fund also encourages unlucky applicants to put their selection on reserve and to apply to The Art Fund for a grant in the usual way. For example, after Art Fund COLLECT in 2008, four grants were awarded towards pieces spotted at the fair. Three went to short-listed applicants and one to an applicant which had not made the shortlist.

This year, the format for applications remains the same. However, we are encouraging applicants to widen their scope even further, fully considering the wonderful variety of international work on offer at COLLECT. In particular, we are asking them to focus on makers who are not only under-represented in their own collections, but in UK collections as a whole.

This is an important initiative which fosters a growing public appetite for contemporary craft. As Lucinda van der Post wrote in The Times last May in her preview of COLLECT, 'Craft, as observant readers will already know, is hot – in the sense that it is creatively flourishing.' I hope that Art Fund COLLECT will continue to do what it has done thus far: encouraging more and better curatorial research, more networking and more acquisitions of the best examples of contemporary craft. We will help to keep contemporary craft flourishing, and the public will enjoy and understand it with ever more enthusiasm.

Dr Stephen Deuchar, Director, The Art Fund

The Crafty Market

1. The shop closed 30 years later
2. Sculpture Object and Functional Art fairs held in New York in April, in Chicago in November, in Santa Fe in July
3. Another is Masterpiece, in Chelsea
4. The European Fine Art Fair, held every March
5. The Arts Council's Own Art scheme can help with financing, and a number of COLLECT exhibitors are registered for the scheme. www.artscouncil.org.uk/ownart

It is often said that when the potter Grayson Perry won the Turner Prize in 2003, the award represented the coming-of-age of craft as an art form on the level with other artistic practices. But in fact the process had started long before; ceramics specialist and COLLECT exhibitor Adrian Sassoon mentions the Crafts Council shop in the Victoria and Albert Museum, opened in 1974,[1] as an 'important step for putting crafts on the map in the UK, because curators came in, and bought pieces for themselves, and it gave the artists a platform they hadn't had before.'

The COLLECT fair is now held in the Saatchi Gallery, between shows of Indian, American or Chinese art, and this is a significant indicator of the evolution of the market for fine craft.

Certainly this market has benefited from the intense interest in contemporary art and 20th-century design characterising this last decade. The process started earlier in the US with its SOFA fairs[2] which began in 1994, their director Mark Lyman is an informal consultant to COLLECT. 'Of course, the tradition of craft as a process goes further back in the UK,' he says, referring to the Arts and Crafts movement.

But today fine craft is no longer confined to specialist events and indeed is increasingly exhibited elsewhere. 'Even the traditional art fairs include 20th-century creations today, and it makes for a far more interesting mix,' says Anna Haughton, organiser of Art Antiques London, one of several contenders for the place of the now defunct Grosvenor House Antiques Fair.[3] In Maastricht, the world's foremost traditional art and antiques fair TEFAF [4] inaugurated TEFAF Design last year, featuring nine specialist dealers. But while craft found a place within the market for 20th-century art, it didn't skyrocket, as contemporary art did during the 2004–2007 boom, nor did it plunge in the same way during the 2008–2009 bust. 'Prices have been stable,' says COLLECT exhibitor Sarah Myerscough. Adrian Sassoon expands: 'While prices don't grow much, the range increases as an artist progresses in his career, and makes more ambitious works which inevitably cost more.'

Most craft is sold on the primary market directly through dealers, and so there is no independent way to evaluate either volume or value. But many dealers note that their sales have been satisfactory despite the recession. According to Matthew Hall of Galerie Besson, 'The level of sales has been maintained, but the strongest demand is for classic works by well known makers.' And, he says, 'buyers are very aware that this is a great time to buy, with the additional advantage that they can negotiate good terms – for instance by making a deal to pay over a number of months.'[5] Myerscough adds: 'The recession has meant that people are more aware of value, and

6. Among them are Woolley & Wallis in Salisbury, UK; Bonhams in London; Wright in Chicago
7. Coper's world record is $60,000 for a *Large Spade Form* from about 1967, which sold at Bonhams New York in June 2007.

they see craft as a bargain compared to contemporary art. Many aspects of technique and process have been lost in contemporary art, but craft pieces are hand-made with skill involved; they take time to produce, and buyers appreciate this.'

As for the secondary or resale market, this goes through dealers and also some auction houses.[6] In London and New York, Phillips de Pury has some craft objects within its Design sales. Its main emphasis is again on Rie and Coper (ceramics), but the firm has also achieved good prices for works by Jim Partridge (wood), Peter Collingswood (textiles) and Ernst Gampel (wood). In October last year, for example, Partridge and Liz Walmsley's oak *Curved Bench* (2002) made a healthy £10,625, over its estimate of £5,500–£6,500, while Collingwood's *3D Macrogauze M30/6* sold for £4,375 (est. £2,000–£3,000) in April last year.

Ben Williams, contemporary ceramics specialist, Design, at Phillips de Pury, also notes the surge of interest in Lucie Rie, driven by Japanese collectors. A major exhibition of her work opened in the Tokyo National Arts Centre on 28 April and will tour to five other venues, while wide publicity in Japan has been given to a Hans Coper touring show. In June last year the highest price ever paid at auction for Rie was for a 1984 stoneware vase in New York, which made $55,000, almost double the $25,000–$35,000 estimate.[7]

'What seems to be happening in the market,' says Williams, 'is a changing of the guard. The traditional, older collectors are taking more of a back seat and are more likely to sell than buy, but a new group of collectors is coming in. They love the objects, but do not necessarily take an academic interest – it's more instinctive,' he says. The market has become 'polarised', he says, with the top pieces maintaining their price levels. And to his surprise, he notes that some auction prices are higher than retail, giving as an example a Gordon Baldwin bowl that made $25,000 in New York in 2008 – such a piece might only be in the £6,000 range in its gallery, Marsden Woo.

While ceramics remain the mainstay of the market, dealers note heightened interest in works that are close to nature – COLLECT exhibitor Yvonna Demczynska of Flow mentions works in wood or basketry by such makers as Hans Henning Pederson or Mary Butcher as being particularly popular. In conclusion, says everyone in the craft world, craft is great value for money, particularly in comparison to the hundreds of thousands needed to buy contemporary art. 'You have to be so wealthy to buy paintings, but look at the work of, say Gordon Baldwin, it is astonishing that you can buy a major work for under £6,000,' concludes Matthew Hall.

Georgina Adam, Art Market Editor at Large, The Art Newspaper

Exhibitors

Second floor

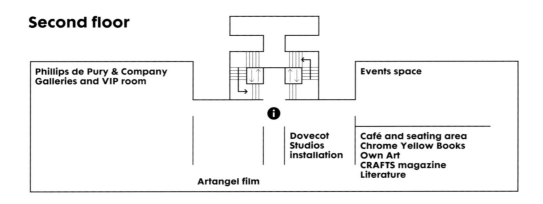

Phillips de Pury & Company Galleries and VIP room

Events space

Dovecot Studios installation

Café and seating area
Chrome Yellow Books
Own Art
CRAFTS magazine
Literature

Artangel film

First floor

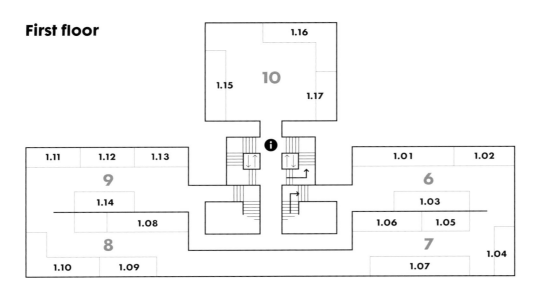

1.16

1.15   10

1.17

1.11   1.12   1.13

9

1.14

1.08

8

1.10   1.09

1.01   1.02

6

1.03

1.06   1.05

7

1.04

1.07

Ground floor

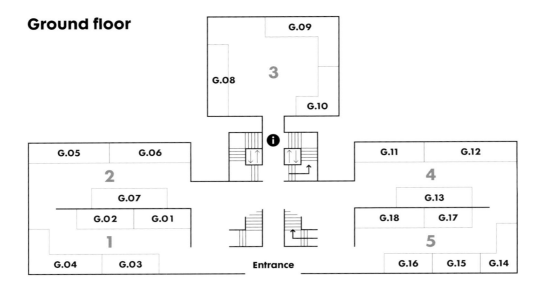

G.09

G.08   3

G.10

G.05   G.06

2

G.07

G.02   G.01

1

G.04   G.03

Entrance

G.11   G.12

4

G.13

G.18   G.17

5

G.16   G.15   G.14

Alternatives Gallery specialises in contemporary jewellery, and is dedicated to the promotion of both internationally established artists and newcomers from all over the world. Located in central Rome since 1997, the gallery hosts 50–60 artists and 5–6 solo or group exhibitions each year.

Staff
Rita Marcangelo, Director

Contact
Via D'Ascanio 19
Rome
Italy 00186
T +39 06683 08233
F +39 06683 08233
E info@alternatives.it
www.alternatives.it

Artists represented
Silvie Altschuler
Adrean Bloomard
Diana Dudek
Maria Rosa Franzin
Hanna Hedman
Mari Ishikawa
Ute Kolar
Marie Louise Kristensen
Margherita Marchioni
Sonia Morel
Kazumi Nagano
Ritsuko Ogura
Giovanni Sicuro
Janna Syvänoja
Michelle Taylor
Fabrizio Tridenti
Graziano Visintin

Hanna Hedman
Pendant, *What you tell is not always what you have experienced*, 2009
H 56 × W 23 × D 14 cm
Silver, oxidised silver, powder-coated copper and paint
Photo: Sanna Lindberg

Hedman is interested in contrasting beauty with the unpleasant, the serious and the not-so-nice. To Hedman, the sad and disgusting can also be beautiful. Beauty is used to catch the viewer's attention, but there is much more that Hedman would like to convey. Themes that often recur in her work are human weakness and underlying defence mechanisms. She tries to keep an open attitude to methods and materials, employing new techniques, combinations and approaches, but at the same time she remains strongly rooted in the past.

Fabrizio Tridenti
Ring, *untitled*, 2009
H 12.5 × W 6 × D 4.5 cm
Bronze scrap melting, acrylic paint
Photo: Fabrizio Tridenti

Tridenti takes inspiration from the waste
produced by contemporary society, often
using industrial waste paint to construct
his jewels. He reformulates and transforms
these materials through the analysis of
chaotic structures; these may have an
aesthetic function, yet at the same time
it is hard to know whether the object
is undergoing construction or decon-
struction. To the artist, waste and disorder
are extremely vibrant and expressive,
and understood as the essence of reality.
Tridenti employs innovative techniques
including soldering elements enamelled
with acrylic paints.

blås&knåda is a co-operative association of nearly 50 professional ceramists and glass-artists. Since 1975, they have run a gallery and shop in Stockholm, showing contemporary ceramics and glass. 10–12 exhibitions are organised in the gallery every year, presenting both Swedish and international artists.

Staff

Boel Widell Henrikson, Curator
Annika Söderqvist, Shop/Economy

Contact

Hornsgatan 26
Stockholm
Sweden SE–118 20
T +46(0)8642 7767
E boel.henrikson@blasknada.com
www.blasknada.com

Artists represented

Anna Carlgren, glass
Ylva W. Franzén, ceramic
Ulla Gustafsson, glass
Anna Höggren, glass
Pernilla Jansson, ceramic
Magdalena Nilsson, ceramic
Carl Richard Söderström, ceramic

Anna Höggren

The Rose-hip, 2008
54 cm long
Free-blown glass
Photo: Anders Roth

'Glass has been my working material for more than 20 years now. It is fragile and at the same time tremendously strong, so must be treated with sensitivity, in both the hot working process and as a finished object. I always try to create simple forms, in order to let the material show its qualities itself. Glass can still surprise me enormously, and offers me great challenges, over and over again. This is a joy!'

Anna Höggren

Carl Richard Söderström

Urn, 2009
H 42 × W 24 cm
Stoneware, decorated with
white slip and glaze
Photo: Carl Richard Söderström

Inspired by orangeries and garden decorations throughout history, decorated with fruits and flowers, gargoyles and skulls, Söderström's unique urns are bold and grotesque, with clear references to Gothic sculpture. Often found filled with flowers, and used as central pieces in still lifes, they are constructed in black stoneware covered in white slip and glaze, sometimes fired up to four times, with many layers of glaze.

The Bluecoat Display Centre has been established 50 years in Liverpool, showing a national and international selection of collectable contemporary applied artists, with regularly changing exhibitions and a supporting education programme as well as a permanent display of over 300 individuals.

Staff

Dr Maureen Bampton, Director
Samantha Rhodes, Assistant Director

Contact

50–51 the Bluecoat
College Lane Entrance
Liverpool
Merseyside
L1 3BZ UK
T +44(0)151 709 4014
E crafts@bluecoatdisplaycentre.com
www.bluecoatdisplaycentre.com

Artists represented

Stephen Bird, ceramic
Michael Brennand-Wood, textile
Stephen Dixon, ceramic
Thomas Hill, metal
Cleo Mussi, ceramic
Emma Rodgers, ceramic/metal
Melanie Tomlinson, metal

Michael Brennand-Wood
Tunes of Glory, 2009
H 85 × W 75 × D 60 cm
Textile and mixed media
Photo: Peter Mennim

Compositionally, Brennand-Wood's *Tunes of Glory* is based on an American arena – a ceremonial or civic space where action unfolds. It acknowledges various aspects of warfare: strategies, war games, the lottery of survival, trench warfare, gun batteries, entanglement and the memorialisation of conflict via the floral tribute. In many ways, *Tunes of Glory* can also be seen as a descendent of *Virtue Rewarded, Vice Punished*, a form of morality board game popular in the early 19th-century.

Stephen Bird
War on Pottery, 2009
H 30 × W 24 × D 19 cm
Ceramic
Photo: Stephen Bird

Originally a painter, Bird has brought
the knowledge he gained about colour
and surface to the dynamic figures and
dioramas he fabricates from ceramic
components. He subverts the 18th- and
19th-century tradition of the Staffordshire
figurine, imbuing it with contemporary
narratives and themes; political belief,
violence, faith and the everyday. His use
of visual clichés, *trompe l'oeil* and surprise
unifies these fragments into objects that
acknowledge their separate and
independent contexts.

Bullseye Gallery works with a select group of international artists in the field of kiln-formed glass, to encourage exceptional design via innovation in material and method.

Staff

Lani McGregor, Executive Director
Jamie Truppi, Assistant Director

Contact

300 NW 13th Avenue
Portland, Oregon
USA 97209
T +1 503 227 0222
F +1 503 227 0008
E gallery@bullseyeglass.com
www.bullseyegallery.com

Artists represented

Karen Akester
Heike Brachlow
Joseph Harrington
Catharine Newell
Jeffrey Sarmiento
April Surgent

Heike Brachlow
Movement VI, 2008
H 37.1 × W 50.8 × D 34.3 cm
Kiln-cast glass
Photo: Michael Endo

'The unexpected. The slightly odd, the surreal, the uncanny. Precariousness. Stability. Equilibrium. Imbalance. Things that are not what they seem. Movement. Things that change. Puzzles. Building blocks. There but not there. Fragile. Solid. Ambiguous. The potential for chaos.'

Heike Brachlow

Joseph Harrington
Latheron, 2009
H 27 × W 14 × D 7.9 cm
Kiln-cast glass, lost ice process
Photo: Stephen Brayne

'I have a fascination with turning one thing into another, and for the reaction of materials and energies as they act on one another. This leads to a spontaneous working method and a creative mindset, with the energy living on within the piece, giving a sense of progression and evolution within a solid, permanent structure. My latest body of work represents landscapes, and the structures within them. I focus on Britain's rugged coastlines and its rural countryside, looking at its erosion as a fascinating spectacle of discovery and generation of form.'

Joseph Harrington

Clare Beck and Adrian Sassoon present contemporary studio ceramics, glass, silver and jewellery, principally British, from museum-quality work to more modestly priced pieces. For COLLECT 2010, we are exhibiting new work made especially for this fair. The display includes large-scale pieces suitable for public spaces, medium-scale objects for the home and a treasury of smaller objects presented in an intimate space. We will also make solo presentations of new work by Kate Malone, Rupert Spira and Hiroshi Suzuki.

Staff

Adrian Sassoon
Clare Beck
Kathleen Slater
Mark Piolet
Andrew Wicks

Contact

(by appointment only)
14 Rutland Gate
London
SW7 1BB UK
T +44(0)207 581 9888
F +44(0)207 823 8473
E email@adriansassoon.com
www.adriansassoon.com

Artists represented

Galia Amsel, glass
Felicity Aylieff, ceramic
Giovanni Corvaja, jewellery
Natasha Daintry, ceramic
Michael Eden, ceramic
Ndidi Ekubia, metal
Elizabeth Fritsch, ceramic
Hitomi Hosono, ceramic
Angela Jarman, glass
Chris Knight, metal
Hans Kotter, glass
Danny Lane, glass
Kate Malone, ceramic
Alistair McCallum, metal
Junko Mori, metal
Adam Paxon, jewellery
Colin Reid, glass
Bruno Romanelli, glass
Kayo Saito, jewellery
Rupert Spira, ceramic
Hiroshi Suzuki, metal
Andrew Wicks, ceramic
Rachael Woodman, glass
Susan Wraight, wood
Udo Zembok, glass

Rupert Spira

Deep Open Bowl, 2009
H 18, Diam. 40 cm
Stoneware, incised text through black pigment over white glaze

Spira's ceramic works convey a sense of clarity and peace. This broad elegant bowl appears to hover on its small foot with an extraordinary balance of form. Expertly thrown, it continues its maker's exploration of a high-contrast, monochromatic palette, with lines of flowing text incised through black pigment over a pure white glaze. Spira has travelled extensively in Japan and the Far East, and his works are widely exhibited and collected by many important international public collections.

Hiroshi Suzuki
Earth-Reki III, 2009
H 27.5, Diam.25 cm
Hammer-raised fine silver 999

Suzuki has an extraordinary talent for
raising silver from single flat sheets to
create vessels full of flowing, vigorous,
graceful lines. As this piece shows, his
work is intuitive and combines traditional
skills with a unique and personal visual
vocabulary. Now highly acclaimed, he
is represented in numerous museums
worldwide. His pieces are often collected
as much for the way they offer continuity
with the history of English silver as for their
striking sense of contemporary luxury.

Cockpit Arts supports and promotes the
work of applied artists and designer-makers
at all stages of their careers – from first
beginnings through to international success.
It is the largest creative community of its
kind in the UK, housing 165 artists in its
2 London studio centres. Artists may be
visited at the studios by appointment.

Staff
Abigail Branagan
Lucy Everett
Vanessa Swann

Contact
Cockpit Yard
Northington Street
London
WC1N 2NP UK
T +44(0)207 419 1959
F +44(0)207 916 2455
E info@cockpitarts.com
www.cockpitarts.com

Artists represented
Kelvin Birk, jewellery
Adele Brereton, jewellery/metal
Ruth Tomlinson, jewellery
Shan Valla, ceramic/glass
Jonathan Wade, ceramic

Jonathan Wade
Construction no.12, 2008
H 20 × W 120 × D 15 cm
Thrown and constructed stoneware
clay, glaze
Photo: Fotofit

Wade's ceramic compositions deploy
shapes that suggest familiar and domestic
forms as well as more ambiguous items.
They are a response to real and mapped
urban landscapes, and the planned or
random groupings of objects therein. They
reference detritus and high design, and
also the living organic aspects and patterns
found in our man-made environments.

Ruth Tomlinson

Encrustations Ring, 2008
H 2.5 × W 2 × D 1 cm
Silver, 18 carat gold, antique glass
beads, found glass (Hackney Diamond),
rough peridot
Photo: Dominic Sweeny

'My interest is in the inherent quality
of materials. Does the rarity of mined
platinum make it more precious than
a piece of wire found in the pavement?
The form and shape of that rusted wire
also has a history, a story to tell. It had
been run over several times to create
a unique form never to be seen again;
this is precious.'

Ruth Tomlinson

Collection, the gallery of Ateliers d'Art de France, is situated in the heart of the Marais in Paris. It showcases contemporary applied arts, exhibiting the work of both established artists and emerging talents, with a wide variety of expertise. It holds 6 exhibitions a year.

Staff

Anne-Laure Roussille, Gallery Manager

Contact

4 rue de Thorigny
Paris
France 75003
T +33(0)142 786774
F +33(0)142 774201
E collection@ateliersdart.com
www.ateliersdart.com

Artists represented

Roland Daraspe, metal
Claire Lindner, ceramic
Alain Mailland, wood

Roland Daraspe

Coupe facettes or, 2009
H 12.5 cm, Diam. 14.4 cm
Silver 925, gold 900/1000

'Using tools he made from Pyrenean boxwood, Daraspe constantly tests the limits of solid silver under the strain of the long process of cold hammering. He approaches utilitarian objects in a designer's manner... This know-how has liberated his design virtuosity, as can be seen from the many sketches where he works out his ideas. Over the years, his contemporary style has gained in purity.'

Laurence Salmon, Ateliers d'art n°48, December 2003

Claire Lindner

Ramipède, 2010
H 42 × W 20 cm
Porcelain

'When you take a mass of soft clay and stretch it from the inside, it enlarges and metamorphoses whilst still retaining traces of the transformations that have been made. The imprints of the surface tense and transform and allow the layers that they cover to appear. What is more, the body that causes the form to move is hidden by the film of clay that conceals it. Thus, all the manipulations and interventions that are engendered by the hand remain imperceptible. The mass remains only thing visible and appears to move and transform by itself, giving the curious impression of being alive.

'Material that comes to life fascinates me. The final form is the result, frozen in time, of a process and a movement where the material is both building and regressing. In this in-between phase, the form has the power to pass from the similar to the dissimilar. The idea of a possible metamorphosis, the notions of a probable beginning and an end, reflect back as well on the living.'

Claire Lindner

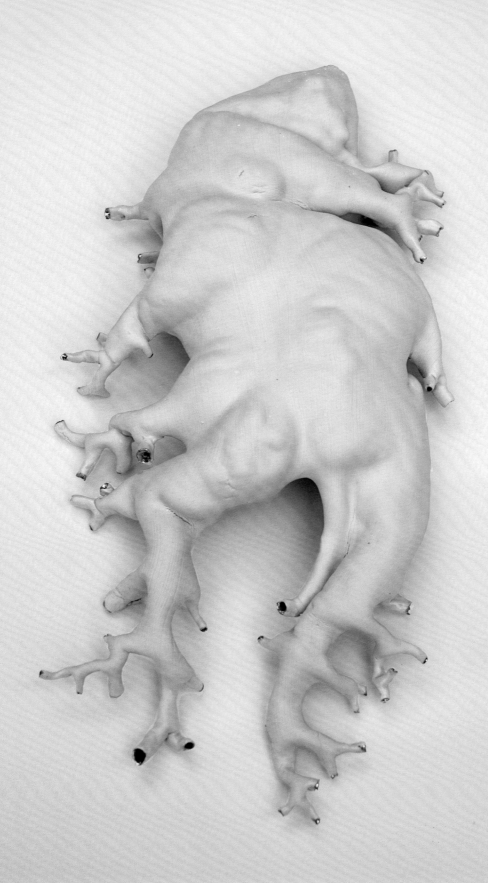

Contemporary Applied Arts is London's largest applied arts gallery, promoting the best of applied art since 1948. The gallery represents over 300 renowned artists working within ceramics, glass, jewellery, metal, silver, textiles and wood.

Staff

Sarah Edwards, Director
Clare Maddison, Retail Manager

Contact

2 Percy Street
London
W1T 1DD UK
T +44(0)207 436 2344
F +44(0)207 636 6269
E sarah.edwards@caa.org.uk
www.caa.org.uk

Artists represented

Zöe Arnold, jewellery
Nick Arroyave-Portela, ceramic
Phil Atrill, glass
Sara Brennan, textile
Helen Carnac, metal
Ane Christensen, metal
Sarah Denny, metal
Stephen Gillies and Kate Jones, glass
Gabriele Koch, ceramic
Drummond Masterton, metal
Craig Mitchell, ceramic
Gareth Neal, furniture
Jacob van der Beugel, ceramic
Katie Walker, furniture

Stephen Gillies and Kate Jones

Parent, 2009
H 35 × W 32 cm
Blown glass, hand-etched
Photo: Pete Chambers

'Our vessels are containers, both metaphorical and literal. We use the transparency and beauty of the medium to communicate our dual interests in making and concept. This most recent body of work continues to explore the expressive potential of the vessel, using universal patterns, forms and themes.'

Stephen Gillies and Kate Jones

Zöe Arnold

Emotions Brooch, Red, 2009
H 7 × W 4.5 cm
Doll's body, diamonds, druzy, garnet, mother of pearl
Photo: Zöe Arnold

Arnold's sensitive pieces are as much artworks as they are exquisite forms of jewellery. Often with a darker side, if the viewer delves beneath the surface, her works stir the thinker's mind and the emotions found there. They take inspiration from many sources, including her own poetry, and experiences of precious metals or collected curios are carved, pierced and worked into wearable artworks, every one telling a different story.

Helen Carnac
Each Other, 2009
H 95 × W 66 × D 66 cm
Steel, copper, vitreous enamel and wood
Photo: David Gates

Carnac is a maker, curator and academic
living and working in London. Central
to her practice as a maker and thinker
are drawing, mark-making, the explicit
connections between material, process and
maker, and an emphasis on deliberation
and reflection.

Jacob van der Beugel
Imposter 2, 2009
H 30 × W 100 × D 40 cm
Stoneware
Photo: Jacob van der Beugel

Van der Beugel creates one-off vessels and
unique ceramic installations. He employs
decoration that pierces traditional
surfaces. His vessels become a metaphor
for the human condition. His installation
pieces are inspired by music scores and
Dutch 17th-century still lifes.

craftscotland, funded by the Scottish Arts Council, is the agency dedicated to developing audiences for Scottish craft. Their website is a gateway to news about Scottish craft, with a searchable directory of Scottish makers plus places to see and buy craft.

Staff

Emma Walker, Chief Executive
Laura Anderson, Online Marketing Officer
Julie Kelly, Project Manager
Rachel McCrum, PhD studentship

Contact

7–9 North St David Street
Edinburgh
Midlothian
EH2 1AW UK
T +44(0)131 524 9424
F +44(0)131 524 9425
E enquiries@craftscotland.org
www.craftscotland.org

Scottish **Arts** Council

Artists represented

Stacey Bentley, jewellery
Leah Black, jewellery
Jilli Blackwood, textile
Libby Day, metal
Pauline Edie, jewellery
Lorna Fraser, ceramic
Elin Isaksson, glass
Rebecca Wilson, ceramic
Misun Won, jewellery

Stacey Bentley

Textured Enamel Series #9, Ring, 2009
H 0.62 × W 0.6 × D 0.45 cm
Silver, iron, enamel, steel
Photo: Stacey Bentley

Bentley explores the new possibilities and ideas that industrial liquid enamel can bring to contemporary jewellery. She challenges preconceptions about technique, process and aesthetic in relation to enamel. Smooth silver wire structures give strength and stability. Intertwined within these are thin enamelled binding wire elements, creating a sense of fragility. With this combination of materials, Bentley creates unpredictable, spontaneous forms of unique textural and painterly quality.

Rebecca Wilson
Finest Paper-ware, 2009
H 16 cm
Ceramic, hand-made paper
Photo: Rebecca Wilson

With the growth of throwaway culture,
our habits of consumption have changed.
Convenience and fashion now take prece-
dence and consumption is increasingly more
about having, using, and discarding objects,
than about saving or cherishing them. With
the disposable paper cup as an icon of this
trend, Wilson has created the Finest Paper-
ware range, which mimics the Wedgwood
style, transposing the ceramic context onto
the throwaway object.

The Cultural Connections CC Gallery promotes, raises awareness of and consolidates the high standard and beauty of Danish Contemporary Ceramics. It is the ancient vessel form in all of its infinite diversity that provides the driving inspiration behind the gallery's presentation of unique studio ceramics from the Nordic countries, showing the techniques in form, material and glazes that the artists constantly strive to develop and achieve.

Staff

Birthe Nørgaard Fraser, Director
Pernille Nørgaard Fraser, Co-ordinator
T. W. Fraser, Co-Director
Jan-Kaare Myklebust, Assistant

Contact

Kylling House
29 Elmtree Green
Great Missenden
Buckinghamshire
HP16 9AF UK
T +44(0)1494 866803
M +44(0)7872 962199
F +44(0)1494 866803
E fraserartconsult@talk21.com
www.culturalconnections.co.uk

Artists represented

Lis Ehrenreich
Gutte Eriksen
Ninna Gøtzsche
Kim Holm
Mette Augustinus Poulsen
Dorte Visby

Dorte Visby

Lidded jar, *Ancient Seabed*, 2009
H 15 × W 22 cm
Saggar-fired ceramic
Photo: Jens Morten

'The surfaces of my work are influenced by the geological structures that appear in the ancient seabed. I create the surfaces working with my fingers and tools; afterwards the clay is stretched, creating slabs by throwing the clay on a table.'

Dorte Visby

Kim Holm
Fire, 2009
H 26 × W 35 cm
Ceramic – cylinder with lustre glaze
Photo: Erik Balle Poûlsen

Holm's work is carefully proportioned.
The simplicity and harmony of the cylinder
is interrupted by subtle works: a squeezed
rim or dent or series of lines. His work
reflects inspiration from Japan and traces
of Danish ceramists like Gutte Eriksen.
This work is based on the Danish value
of good craftsmanship, of the appeal of
the simple forms, or ornamentation and
colour scheme inspired by nature.

Dovecot Studios is a specialist contemporary tapestry studio working with international artists and designers on commissions and special projects. Dovecot is based at the heart of the Dovecot Building, a new art space in Edinburgh dedicated to championing art, craftsmanship and contemporary design.

Staff

David Weir, Director
Emily Pelham Burn, Studio Manager
Francesca Baseby, Gallery Manager

Weaving team

Douglas Grierson
David Cochrane
Naomi Robertson
Jonathan Cleaver

Contact

Dovecot
10 Infirmary Street
Edinburgh
EH1 1LT UK
T +44 (0)131 550 3660
F +44 (0)131 550 3669
E info@dovecotstudios.com
www.dovecotstudios.com

Artist

Claire Barclay, tapestry/installation

'Barclay sees making as a cerebral as well as a physical process, a way to think through the potential of a material, a form and an idea, developing and intertwining them along the way. She is interested in how a skilled craftsperson understands materials, and in how a finished form bears witness to that understanding.'

Fiona Bradley, Director
Fruitmarket Gallery, Edinburgh

Dovecot occupies unusual territory – a world of skilled craftsmanship, making and design together with a wide range of artistic influence – including photographers, sculptors, fashion designers, painters and, of course, weavers. The collaboration with Claire Barclay offers both artist and studio an opportunity to explore meaningfully that relationship and to create a sculptural installation with tapestry an integral part of the work.

Opposite: photographs by Shannon Tofts

Electrum Gallery is the premier international jewellery gallery in London. Promoting contemporary jewellery since 1971, it hosts 7 exhibitions a year, featuring new and established international artists.

Staff

Sarah Edwards, Director
Flora Bhattachary, Manager
Siân Matthews

Contact

21 South Molton Street
London
W1K 5QZ UK
T +44(0)207 629 6325
F +44(0)207 629 9019
E sales@electrumgallery.co.uk
www.electrumgallery.co.uk

Artists represented

Anna Osmer Anderson
Susan Cross
Charlotte de Syllas
Gerda Flöckinger CBE
Castello Hansen
Bryan Illsley
Daphne Krinos
Tithi Kutchamuch
Susan May
Maria Militsi
Jacqueline Mina
Tom and Jutta Munsteiner
Angela O'Kelly
Nathalie Perneel
Lina Peterson
Paul Preston
Axel Russmeyer
Rie Taniguchi

Castello Hansen

Brooch, 2009
H 5 cm
Red Japanese lacquer
Photo: Castello Hansen

'Jewellery as a phenomenon, its culture, its history, its visual and tactile aspects, wrapped up in the sensation of wearing a piece: all the substance to the conception in my work comes "of" jewellery.'

Castello Hansen

Angela O'Kelly

Neckpiece, Red, Blue and Gold, 2009
H 36 × W 33 cm
Paper and gold leaf
Photo: Trevor Hart

O'Kelly is an artist whose wearable art pieces cross the boundaries between jewellery, sculpture and textile art, combining paper with fabric, felt, metal, cord, recycled plastic and semi-precious stones, using a variety of textile and jewellery techniques. She produces two ranges: large sculptural wearable art pieces and a range of smaller neckpieces, brooches and bangles.

Flatland Gallery is a Dutch contemporary art gallery founded in 1983. The gallery is acclaimed for its international stance, and enjoys a high reputation for the talented contemporary Dutch artists it has brought to the fore of the international art scene.

Staff

Martin Rogge, Director/Owner
Willem de Poorter, Director Sales and Fairs
Fiona van Schendel, Editorial and Communication
Lize Kraan, Gallery Assistant

Contact

Lange Nieuwstraat 7
The Netherlands 3512 PA
T + 31(0)30 231 5181
F + 31(0)30 236 8424

78 Rue Amelot
Paris
France 75011
T + 31(0)654 964 664
E info@flatlandgallery.com
www.flatlandgallery.com

Artists represented

Janpeter Muilwijk, textile
Carolein Smit, ceramic

Janpeter Muilwijk
Floating man, 2009
H 1.53 × W 2.4 m
Silk and linen, Jacquard woven tapestry
Photo: Jan Tregot
Courtesy Flatland Gallery (Utrecht, Paris)

Muilwijk is a religious artist whose work is often directly adapted from the Bible. His delicate drawings with light pencil are transmuted into Jacquard woven art tapestries, reminding us of early Christian culture – but equally are an ode to simple uncomplicated happiness. Muilwijk feels his images render comfort in a world come adrift – renewal has become a goal in itself.

Carolein Smit
Arieshead, 2009
H 23 × W 27 × D 54 cm
Ceramics
Photo: Winnifred Limburg
Courtesy Flatland Gallery (Utrecht, Paris)

Smit plays with that unknown turning point where beauty turns over into exuberance, hate into love, alienation into elucidation. She borrows themes from classic mythology and Biblical tales, such as greed, power, impotence and vanity, but never omits her own touch of irony.

Flow was established in October 1999
by Yvonna Demczynska, to showcase both
British and international contemporary
crafts. Located in the heart of Notting Hill,
London, the gallery holds 6 exhibitions
a year.

Staff

Yvonna Demczynska, Managing Director
Rebecca Dean, Gallery Assistant
Lisa Stockham, Gallery Assistant

Contact

1–5 Needham Road
London
W11 2RP UK
T +44(0)207 243 0782
F +44(0)207 792 1505
E info@flowgallery.co.uk
www.flowgallery.co.uk

Artists represented

Trine Drivsholm, glass
Lizzie Farey, basketry
Aino Kajaniemi, textile
Benben Li, ceramic
Wiebke Meurer, metal
Piet Stockmans, ceramic

Aino Kajaniemi

Installation of 14 pieces, *Touch*, 2008,
1.5 × 1.2 m
Textile, tapestry, linen, cotton, wool, silk
Photo: Aino Kajaniemi

'My textiles are the result of my mind's
wanderings. I weave pictures using a
tapestry technique, with the human figure
in all its complexity at the centre. I aspire
for a little order in a chaotic world. My
small tapestries are like line drawings;
black lines on white, white lines on black,
and all the tones between them.'

Aino Kajaniemi

Lizzie Farey
Flock, 2009
Diam. 1.32 m
Willow
Photo: Shannon Tofts

'Farey uses organic materials to construct
fluid and elegant "wall drawings", where
each willow strand is akin to the line of
a pencil inscription. Her purpose here
is to demonstrate movement through the
fewest individual components and present
a narrative through the gestural line.'

Professor Simon Olding, 2009

Established in 1988, Galerie Besson has a world-wide reputation for exhibiting international contemporary and 20th-century studio ceramics. In addition to mounting 10 exhibitions a year, the gallery also attends art fairs in New York and Chicago.

Staff
Anita Besson, Owner
Matthew Hall
Louisa Anderson

Contact
15 Royal Arcade
28 Old Bond Street
London
W1S 4SP UK
T +44(0)20 7491 1706
F + 44(0)20 7495 3203
E enquiries@galeriebesson.co.uk
www.galeriebesson.co.uk

Artists represented
Claudi Casanovas
Hans Coper
Bernard Dejonghe
Jennifer Lee
Jacqueline Lerat
Shozo Michikawa
Gwyn Hanssen Pigott
Lucie Rie

Jennifer Lee
Olive, umber and dark haloed bands, tilted shelf rim, 2009
H 24.3 × W 14.2 cm
Hand-built coloured stoneware
Photo: Alan Tabor

'Caught between movement and stillness, their fine, standing forms appear simultaneously rooted yet weightless, both silent and exerting considerable presence, holding within themselves a concentrated energy. It is work that shows an extraordinary attunement to materials, an intense and committed relationship through which forms are painstakingly brought into being. And whether of classical profile or animated through disruptions to their contours, the resulting forms remain strong, balanced, and resolved.'

Alun Graves, taken from his own essay for the catalogue of Jennifer Lee, Galerie Besson, 2008; Graves is curator of the ceramics and glass collection at the Victoria and Albert Museum.

Jacqueline Lerat
Trois doigts carrés jaunes, 2002
H 37 × W 23.5 × D 8.5 cm
Wood-fired stoneware
Photo: Alan Tabor

'Jacqueline Lerat (1920–2008) fascinated
me by her personality and the power of her
work. Her 2007 exhibition was one of the
most moving shows I have held. Her very
last words to Bernard Dejonghe, the day
before she died, were "Les sculpteurs
travaillent sur le plein, les céramistes
travaillent sur le vide: c'est très important"
(Sculptors work on the solid, ceramists
work on the void: this is very important).'

Anita Besson

Galerie Louise Smit specialises in contemporary studio jewellery. The all-encompassing nature of the gallery demonstrates the latest developments of the national and international avant-garde.

Staff
Louise Smit
Monika Zampa
Evert Nijland
Robert Smit

Contact
Prinsengracht 615
1016 HT Amsterdam
The Netherlands
T +31(0)20 625 9898
E gls@xs4all.nl
www.louisesmit.nl

Artists Represented
Ralph Bakker
Doris Betz
Helen Britton
Iris Eichenberg
Beppe Kessler
Iris Nieuwenburg
Evert Nijland
Mette Saabye
Robert Smit
Terhi Tolvanen
Estela Saèz Vilanova
Christoph Zellweger

Terhi Tolvanen
Brooch, *Gouttes*, 2009
H 9 cm
Labradorite, wood, silver
Photo: Eddo Hartmann

'In my work I visualise the relationship between man and nature. I am fascinated by human interference, the traces left by humankind's taking care, organisation or controlling of nature. Yet nature fights back, it keeps growing and changing. This unpredictable power of life is for me a source of inspiration: the dialogue between control and freedom has become the prevailing theme for my jewellery.'

Terhi Tolvanen

Evert Nijland
Necklace, *Carneool*, 2009
Diam. 15 cm
Glass, silk, carneool, silver
Photo: Eddo Hartmann

Evert Nijland graduated from the Jewellery department at the Gerrit Rietveld Academy in Amsterdam in 1995, followed by a second phase education in the applied Arts at the Sandberg Institute in Amsterdam where he got his Master degree in 1997. He lives and works in Amsterdam, the Netherlands.

Evert Nijland's jewellery has its roots in images from Art history. In particular he has focused on the Renaissance and Baroque periods. However he is not copying the items in the paintings or sculptures, but translating these images into his own contemporary context. He is fascinated by the way nature is visualised by artists across art history. His latest work is called *Naturae* from 2009, and is inspired by the many floral motives that are used in classical ornaments.

Galerie Marzee has been built up over the last 30 years by Marie-José van den Hout. Its home is in Nijmegen in the Netherlands, in a four-storey former grainstore on the banks of the river Waal: an amazing centre for contemporary jewellery.

Staff

Marie-José van den Hout, Director

Contact

Lage Markt 3 – Waalkade 4
Nijmegen
The Netherlands NL–6511 VK
T +31(0)24 3229670
E mail@marzee.nl
www.marzee.nl

Artists represented

Iris Bodemer
Sara Borgegård
Antje Bräuer
Yu-Chun Chen
Willemijn de Greef
Mareen Alburg Duncker
Ute Eitzenhöfer
Kathleen Fink
Ineke Heerkens
Idiots
Stephanie Jendis
Karin Johansson
Beate Klockmann
Rudolf Kocéa
Winfried Krüger
Erik Kuiper
Okinari Kurokawa
Stefano Marchetti
Christine Matthias
Julie Mollenhauer
Carla Nuis
Barbara Paganin
Ruudt Peters
Annelies Planteijdt
Dorothea Prühl
Ulrich Reithofer
Tabea Reulecke
Sybille Richter
Philip Sajet
Lucy Sarneel
Ann Schmalwasser
Karin Seufert
Vera Siemund
Etsuko Sonobe
Tore Svensson
Julia Walter
Florian Weichsberger

Stefano Marchetti
Brooch, 2008
H 8 × W 6.3 × D 1.8 cm
Stainless steel, gold, silver epoxy
Photo: Stefano Marchetti

'I am sure that the most important concept when I create a jewel is how I did it. Every jewel has its own particular way of being created, which has nothing to do with the final result. You could compare it to sport: on one hand, you can cover 100 metres by running really fast and arriving in few seconds, or you can walk slowly, covering the 100 metres in many hours. The important thing in my philosophy is not where, but how.'

From an interview with Bianca Cappello, from 'Failure is an important way of growing up' in Arte y joya, November 2007

Philip Sajet
Necklace, *La Campagna*, 2008
H 29 × W 23 × D 3 cm
Rock crystal, coloured agate, gold
Photo: Beate Klockmann

Paul Derrez has been the enthusiastic force behind Galerie Ra since 1976. Continuity, quality and innovation are the cornerstone of the gallery's international exhibition programme, its eclectic collection and special events. The gallery specialises in jewellery design, with an increasing focus on all types of vessels. Ra serves its public by constantly offering the unpredictable rather than the trite and commonplace.

Staff
Paul Derrez
Willem Hoogstede
Miecke Oosterman

Contact
Vijzelstraat 80
1017 HL
Amsterdam
Netherlands
T +31(0)20 626 5100
F +31(0)20 620 4595
E mail@galerie-ra.nl
www.galerie-ra.nl

Artists represented
Melanie Bilenker, jewellery
Julie Blyfield, jewellery/vessels
Sigurd Bronger, jewellery
Chien-Wei Chang, vessels
Maike Dahl, silver vessels
Sam Tho Duong, jewellery
Warwick Freeman, jewellery
Karl Fritsch, jewellery
Christine Graf, vessels
Michael Haas, silver vessels
Gésine Hackenberg, jewellery
Therese Hilbert, jewellery
Mirjam Hiller, jewellery
Peter Hoogeboom, jewellery
Esther Knobel, jewellery
Nel Linssen, jewellery
Eva Reidel, silver vessels
Constanze Schreiber, jewellery
Bettina Speckner, jewellery
Catherine Truman, jewellery

Mirjam Hiller
Brooch, *Myphelas*, 2009
H 14 × W 10 × D 4 cm
Stainless steel, powder coating
Photo: Mirjam Hiller

…the fascination for man-made constructions…

…the inspiration coming from flora, with its never-ending variety and depth of detail…

…the boundless wealth and complexity of emotions…

…the enthusiasm for simplicity behind complex structures…

…the necessity to explore the balance between total control and unconscious development…

…the permanent longing for intensity and enchantment…

…the craving to see what is filling me up inside taking shape in my hands…

all this allows my jewellery to grow.

Mirjam Hiller

Julie Blyfield
Vessel, *Tinder*, 2008
H 9.5 × W 11 × D 11 cm
Oxidised bronze, enamel paint, wax
Photo: Grant Hancock

'During the long summer months in
Adelaide, South Australia, I experienced
the severe hot and tinder-dry conditions
of a drought. In January 2008, a raging
bushfire roared across Flinders Chase on
Kangaroo Island for more than a week.
I later photographed the devastated
landscape of blackened skeletal mallee
trees silhouetted against the thick, ashen
grey ground cover and the rust, ochre and
soft peach colours of the scorched bush.
Elements of this burnt landscape informed
the creation of my vessels and objects.'

Julie Blyfield

Galerie Rob Koudijs specialises in contemporary art jewellery which communicates ideas, has sculptural qualities and an innovative use of materials. The gallery represents a motivated group of jewellery artists who produce work challenging the borders of the applied and the fine arts. The latest international developments are on display in regular solo shows and in the permanent collection of the gallery.

Staff
Rob Koudijs
Ward Schrijver
Bob de Waal

Contact
Elandsgracht 12
1016 TV Amsterdam
The Netherlands
T +31(0)20 331 8796
M +31(0)6 139 05 554
E info@galerierobkoudijs.nl
www.galerierobkoudijs.nl

Artists represented
Tobias Alm
Alexander Blank
Sebastian Buescher
Gemma Draper
Jantje Fleischhut
Javier Moreno Frías
Hans Hovy
Jiro Kamata
Ted Noten
Katja Prins
Felieke van der Leest
Roos van Soest
Francis Willemstijn

Francis Willemstijn
Necklace , *Gone with the wind*, 2009
Diam.19 cm
Silver, hair, onyx, jet, glass, textile
Photo: Francis Willemstijn

Willemstijn's jewellery is proof of the strength of the cultural heritage in the Netherlands, and how it can be renewed for our own times. For an exhibition in 2009 at the Zuiderzeemuseum Enkhuizen, Willemstijn developed new work based on Dutch customs and traditional costume. These impressive jewellery pieces are a connection between past and present, between tradition and innovation.

Ted Noten
Object, *Grandma's bag revisited*, 2009
H 30 × W 30 × D 6 cm
Louis Vuitton bag, acrylic, chameleon
Photo: Atelier Ted Noten

Noten's work is a radically contemporary
approach of the age-old craft of the
goldsmith. His use of state-of-the-art
technology makes him one of the leading
jewellery artists from the Netherlands.
He will present his latest acrylic objects,
and will also show new ventures in
computer-based production techniques:
jewellery made of nylon and gold, specially
designed for COLLECT.

Galerie Sofie Lachaert

Introspective research in the fields of
contemporary jewellery, design and crafts:
objects as art, art as an object – questioning
function and representation, carefully
selected objects communicate with space,
table and the human body.

Staff
Luc d'Hanis, Owner
Sofie Lachaert, Director

Contact
St Jozefstraat 30 B–9140 Tielrode
Zwartezustersstraat 20 B–9000 Gent
Belgium
T +32(0)3711 1963
E info@lachaert.com
www.lachaert.com

Artists represented
Giampaolo Babetto, metal/jewellery
David Bielander, jewellery
Bram Boo, furniture/metal
Helen Britton, jewellery
Klaus Burgel, jewellery
Lin Cheung, metal/jewellery
Annemie De Corte, jewellery
Tine De Ruysser, jewellery
Luc d'Hanis, furniture/ceramic/silver
Sasa Fumie, jewellery
Pilar Garrigosa, jewellery
Thalia Georgoulis, metal
Ruth Gurvich, ceramic
Anna Heindl, jewellery
David Huycke, metal
John Iversen, jewellery
Charles Kaisin, furniture
Astrid Keller, jewellery
Anna Lang, jewellery/metal
Barbara Paganin, jewellery
Salima Thakker, jewellery
Keith Tyssen, metal
Flora Vagi, wood/jewellery

Giampaolo Babetto
Bracelet, 2009
H 10 × W 8 × D 8 cm
Gold, niello

'Without a doubt Babetto is an important
member of a small but very influential
group of contemporary goldsmiths who
have been making authentic contributions
to the development of their craft. His
jewelled creations are always characterised
by a sense of great delicacy, sustained by
an exemplary technique. His works are
full of hidden and clever touches, with
delightful transformations of shape and
surface and eloquent homages to gold.
Few contemporary artists have used their
materials so effectively. I think that among
those of his generation, Babetto is the
Italian goldsmith *par excellence* and one of
the best in Europe. A jeweller, a goldsmith,
and an extraordinary artist.'

David Watkins

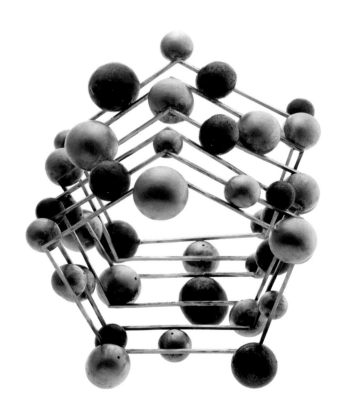

Luc d'Hanis
Anamorphosis, 2008
H 30 × W 35 × D 35 cm
Silver, porcelain
Photo: Joris Luyten

As the ancient Greeks and Romans knew, polished silver has the qualities of an excellent mirror – and thus a silver bottle for liquids can also be a cylindrical mirror. Placed beside an unrecognisably distorted hand-painted water-colour image, it reveals precious, protected birds. This reflection mirrors d'Hanis's deep concern for the threatened extinction of species. The 16th-century distortion technique is called *anamorphosis*: a distortion seen on a plane surface, a drawing or painting, only shows its true shape when seen in a cylindrical mirror placed close to the image.

Galleria Norsu concentrates on the finest in innovative Nordic applied art, both sculptural and functional, including jewellery, ceramics, textiles, wood and glassware.

Staff

Katarina Siltavuori
Saara Kaatra

Contact

Kaisaniemenkatu 9
PO BOX 152
FI-00171 Helsinki, Finland
T   +358(0)9 2316 3250
E   galleria@norsu.info
www.norsu.info

Artists represented

Markku Kosonen, wood
Mervi Kurvinen, jewellery
Nathalie Lahdenmäki, ceramic
Helena Lehtinen, jewellery
Eija Mustonen, jewellery
Kati Nulpponen, jewellery
Maria Nuutinen, jewellery
Tuulia Penttilä, wood
Kim Simonsson, ceramic
Tarja Tuupanen, jewellery

Maria Nuutinen

Bracelet, *Prayer*, 2009
H 2 cm, Diam. 10 cm
Coverable buttons, elastic band,
iron-printed fabric, ribbon
Photo: Maria Nuutinen

'I enjoy being surrounded by objects. Everyday objects that have seen life are closer to my heart than hard, shiny modern objects. I traipse around flea markets not to feed a hunger for nostalgia but rather to find human stimuli. Teeth marks, cracks, missing parts and faded colours are all part of life and keep my brain active. The most extraordinary tales and fates emerge from real life. Truth is indeed stranger than fiction.'

Maria Nuutinen

Tuulia Penttilä
Handbag, *Snow White*, 2004
H 34 × W 24.5 × D 5 cm
Birch, plywood, steel
Photo: Sade Kahra

'I build silent objects. I want to design
objects as life partners, silent poems of
the everyday that produce soundless joy
around themselves.'

Tuulia Penttilä

Galleri Format is located in Norway, in the cities of Oslo and Bergen, and represents over 360 arts and crafts artists. All of the artists are hand-picked by a jury, which guarantees the high quality of the works of art. The owner of the gallery is the Norwegian Association for arts and crafts.

Staff
Karianne Helen Sand, Director
Camilla Børresen, Assistant

Contact
Rådhusgata 24
0151 Oslo
Norway
T +47(0)22 41 45 40/43

Vågsalmenningen 12
N–5014 Bergen
Norway
T +47(0)55 30 48 90/91

E oslo@format.no
E karianne.sand@format.no
E bergen@format.no
www.format.no

Artists represented
Hedda Bjerkeli, jewellery
Heidi Bjørgan, ceramic
Elise Hatlø, jewellery
Helene Josefsen Linkosuonio, jewellery
Monica Marcella, ceramic
Inger Johanne Rasmussen, textile
Anna Talbot, jewellery

Heidi Bjørgan
Pink jug, 2007
H 27 × W 18 cm
Porcelain, rubberband
and a secondhand bird
Photo: Heidi Bjørgan

'I am a ceramist and I collect the over-looked objects: like a lamp, an old bread tin or knick-knacks of low value discarded as trash or ending up in a car boot sale. I give these forms a second chance in a new guise, in a new context and sometimes I even add a new function. As a maker my aim is through sampling and remaking to explore the aesthetic potential of the shapes of these objects.'

Heidi Bjørgan

Inger Johanne Rasmussen
Flood, 2009
H 2.13 × W 2.73 m
Textile intarsia, hand-stitched and hand-dyed. Woolen cloth, vliseline and solidott
Photo: Espen Tollefsen

'At COLLECT I will present a retelling of a textile pattern first created by Anna Maria Garthwaite, an 18th-century heroine of mine. I retell stories through dramatisations, enlargements, estrangements and contrasts. My goal is to present genuinely beautiful things, but also things that are fraught with difficulty. I work in a textile-intarsia technique: felted wool is hand-coloured, cut into thousands of pieces and assembled like a puzzle. The pieces are then sewn together by hand.'

Inger Johanne Rasmussen

The aim of Gallery Kunst1 is to show contemporary crafts by leading artists. The gallery endeavours to show works that are interesting and have character, rather than pursue any specific direction or movement in crafts.

Staff

Henning L. Mortensen, Manager

Contact

Sandviksveien 155
N-1337 Sandvika
Norway
T +47(0)472 44 572
E henning@kunst1.no
www.kunst1.no

Artists represented

Millie Behrens, jewellery
Liv Blaavarp, jewellery
Tor Alex Erichsen, ceramic
Ingjerd Hanevold, jewellery
Sidsel Hanum, ceramic
Torbjorn Kvasboe, ceramic
Nanna Melland, jewellery
Tovelise Roekke-Olsen, ceramic
Caroline Slaatte, ceramic
Leif Stangebye Nilsen, metal

Torbjorn Kvasboe
Stack, 2009
H 78 × W 53 cm
English terracotta clay, cylindric elements from manual extruder, shaped and modelled over a centre bottom thrown cone. Leadbisilikat frit/copper glaze. Electric fired.
Photo: Hanna Toensberg

'Between clay and mind: *The Green Stack* is a reflection that plays with the vessel form, a classic vessel shape, made by cylinders, in a spiral pattern form. It is also a body, a three-dimensional torso with gestures and states of mind. The clay material offers a lot of resistance, and I get to know more of the forces over which I have no control; the incalculable elements in my inner being. Emotional discharges become embodiment of feelings, and the works become actual experiences themselves.'

Torbjorn Kvasboe

Liv Blaavarp
Necklace, *North*, 2009
Diam. c.30 cm
Stained bird cherry, horn of reindeer,
camel bone, gold
Photo: A. Roenning

'My essential and constant goal is to
combine a sculptural quality of jewellery
with the wearer's need for functionality.
Natural forms are constructed by joining
the various elements in a logical, numerical
sequence. My jewellery creates sensuality
by means of structured calculation and
soft flowing shapes that change as you
move or re-arrange the piece on your body.'

Liv Blaavarp

Gallery S O's main focus is the contemporary object, able through an inherent grace of form and materials to convey diverse narratives reflecting not trends and styles but the attitudes and expressive intentions of the artist or maker.

Staff
Felix Flury
Antoinette vonder Mühll

Contact
92 Brick Lane
London
E1 6RL UK
T +44(0)207 3778008
E info@galleryso.com
www.galleryso.com

Artists represented
Peter Bauhuis, jewellery
David Clarke, metal
Christian Gonzenbach, jewellery
Andi Gut, jewellery
Kimiaki Kageyama, jewellery
Mah Rana, jewellery
Michael Rowe, metal
Bernhard Schobinger, jewellery
Hans Stofer, jewellery/metal
Simone ten Hompel, metal
Manuel Vilhena, jewellery

Manuel Vilhena
Brooch, no title, 2009
H 12.5 × W 10 × D 3 cm
Juniper, Shakudo, Fine gold,
yellow gold 750, Inox
Photo: Felix Flury

'The work of Vilhena brings storytelling to contemporary jewellery. Stories told as in days of old, little to do with the teller but all to do with the listener – and told not with words, which may deceive, but with colours, shapes and movement, opening wide the doors of personal meaning.'

Ozra Kallian's PhD, Istanbul, 2009

David Clarke
deep spoon, 2009
H 6 × W 2 × D 8 cm
Silver, pewter
Photo: David Clarke

'Silversmithing's conservatism really pushes me to become more creative, challenging and playful. It is essential to keep this discipline alive and forward-thinking. To adapt unwanted, unvalued objects and give them a new life and opportunity is to make them relevant once again. It is essential to push the boundaries and the potential for the discipline, and to raise questions and innovate through making.'

David Clarke

Australia's foremost contemporary glass gallery, promoting emerging and established artists since 1982.

Staff

Maureen Cahill, Gallery Director

Contact

70 Glebe Point Road
Glebe
Sydney NSW 2037
Australia
T +61(0)295 521 552
F +61(0)295 521 552
E mail@glassartistsgallery.com.au
www.glassartistsgallery.com.au

Artists represented

Jasper Dowding
Kevin Gordon
Tevita Havea
Edison Osorio Zapata

Jasper Dowding
Offering Bowl, 2009
H 8 × W 38 × D 38 cm
Blown glass
Photo: Ian Hobbs

Dowding's work is a unique exploration of form and colour, in which he creates startlingly pure and elegant objects. His use of colour overlay to create a vibrant internal/external dialogue has been a consistent theme. With the addition of advanced cold-working techniques Dowding has combined optical elements to create a new and exciting series.

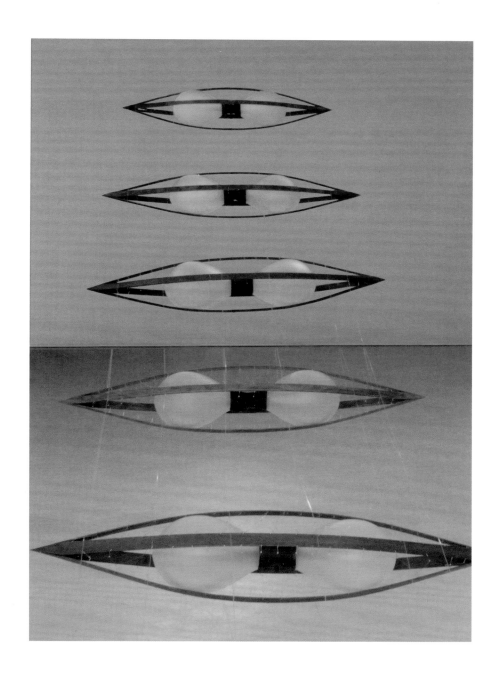

Tevita Havea
Vaka Ika, 2009
Individual pieces: H 21 × W 132 × D 21 cm
Blown glass, wood, fish hooks.
Photo: Julie Green

'Tongan born Tevita Havea explores
and reconciles the polarities of his
Pacific Islander heritage and his current
Western/urban existence (in Sydney),
by making work that underscores the
mutual inclusivity of both. His work
lyrically interweaves Tongan mythology,
creation stories and custom; stories
about regeneration and the symbiotic
relationship between the feminine
and masculine.'

Megan Bottari (from *Modern Primitive*)

Joanna Bird Pottery shows spectacular work from international contemporary ceramic and glass artists, drawn from the traditional and unusual. Pioneer masters are also shown, to give historical perspective, including Hans Coper and Lucie Rie.

Staff

Joanna Bird, Owner/Director
Camilla Webb Carter, Assistant

Contact

19 Grove Park Terrace
London
W4 3QE UK
T +44(0)20 8995 9960
F +44(0)20 8995 9960
E joanna@joannabirdpottery.com
www.joannabirdpottery.com

Artists represented

Danlami Aliyu, ceramic
Richard Batterham, ceramic
Svend Bayer, ceramic
Michael Cardew, ceramic
Fernando Casasempere, ceramic
Carina Ciscato, ceramic
Joanna Constantinidis, ceramic
Hans Coper, ceramic
Steffen Dam, glass
Pippin Drysdale, ceramic
Sueharu Fukami, ceramic
Shoji Hamada, ceramic
Bernard Leach, ceramic
Lucie Rie, ceramic
Annie Turner, ceramic

Pippin Drysdale
Sulphur Springs, 2009
H 17.5–44 cm, Diam. 10–28 cm
Thrown porcelain with inlaid coloured lines
Photo: Robert Frith

Over the last quarter century Drysdale has been refining forms, materials and colour palette to create a unique body of work that is a response to various landscapes. Although an urban artist, she seeks out places that have a special character or resonance, such as the Tanami Desert in central northern Western Australia or the Hunsa Valley at the end of Karakoram Highway in Pakistan.

Steffen Dam
Specimen Panel, 2009
H 50.8 × W 50.8 × D 20.3 cm
Glass
Photo: Anders Bach

'In my first decade of glass making, experiment led me to discover a new kind of beauty in the area of mistakes and faults. In the unwanted air bubble, ash marks, soot, cracks and crookedness I found things that could not be predicted or sketched beforehand. I set the established and traditional techniques aside and started making glass all "wrong" in an attempt to capture the good in the bad. Out of these experiments came the *Fossil*, *Plants* and other such objects – like frozen extracts of chaos to be watched undisturbed.'

Steffen Dam

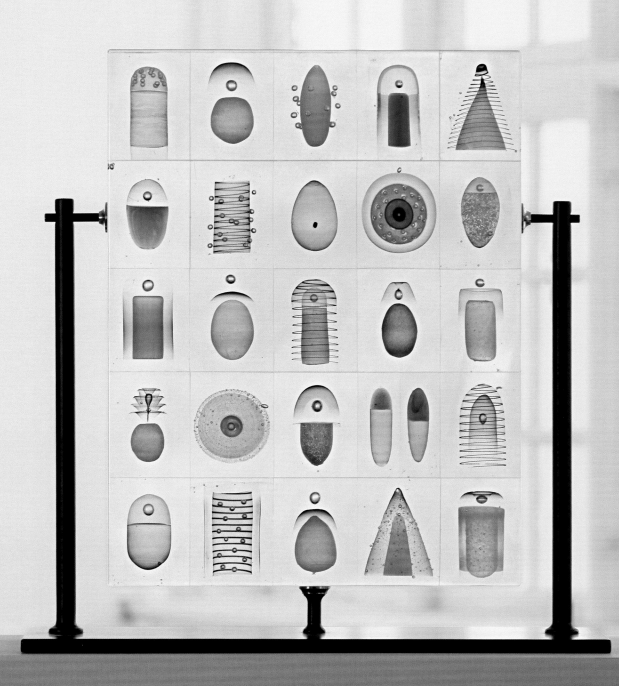

Katie Jones represents contemporary artists from Japan: while the chosen artists have a thoroughly modern outlook, they retain that indefinable Japanese aesthetic.

Staff

Katie Jones, Director
Lesley Mallyon, Assistant

Contact

(by appointment only)
68 Elgin Mansions
Elgin Avenue
London
W9 1JN UK
T +44(0)207 289 1855
F +44(0)207 289 1855
E info@katiejonesjapan.com
www.katiejonesjapan.com

Artists represented

Shihoko Fukumoto, textile
Koji Hatakeyama, metal
Hyoe Imai, ceramic
Hiroki Iwata, metal
Toru Kaneko, metal
Chieko Katsumata, ceramic
Eiko Kishi, ceramic
Ritsue Mishima, glass
Hajime Nakatomi, bamboo
Shouchiku Tanabe, bamboo
Shinya Yamamura, lacquer

Hajime Nakatomi
Ripples under the Bridge, 2007
H 28 × W 97 × D 23 cm
Bamboo
Photo: Matt Pia

'My pieces straddle traditional and contemporary styles of bamboo art. I believe the two styles have a good effect on each other, and my experience has brought me contentment and a new phase in my creativity, allowing me to know what I am and what the world is around me. I can communicate with many people through my pieces, as I realise the natural world through bamboo.'

Hajime Nakatomi

Hyoe Imai
Untitled, 2009
H 21.5 × W 33 × D 33 cm
Ceramic
Photo: Matt Pia

'The key elements in art ceramics are
"restriction" and "materials". One can only
bring out one's self in restriction, never
against an unlimited ground. Ceramic,
meanwhile, is a material with the potential
to transform in various ways through
firing. I hope to create pieces that are close
to supreme abstraction in the forms of
pots (*utsuwa*) by addressing these two
elements positively.'

Hyoe Imai

Lesley Craze Gallery has established a substantial reputation as one of the foremost contemporary jewellery galleries in Europe. The gallery promotes work by more than 100 UK and international designers exhibiting work from both established names to recent graduates. The gallery hosts 4 major exhibitions a year, always including at least 1 featuring international artists.

Staff

Lesley Craze, Managing Director
Rebecca Sweeting, Manager

Contact

33–35a Clerkenwell Green
London
EC1R 0DU UK
T +44(0)20 7608 0393
F +44(0)20 7251 5655
E info@lesleycrazegallery.co.uk
www.lesleycrazegallery.co.uk

Artists represented

Michael Becker, jewellery
Vladimir Bohm, metal
Nora Fok, jewellery
Jo Hayes-Ward, jewellery
Professor Yasuki Hiramatsu, jewellery/metal
Benjamin Lignel, jewellery
Salome Lippuner, jewellery
Wendy Ramshaw CBE RDI, jewellery
Kamilla Ruberg, jewellery
Maud Traon, jewellery
Arek Wolski, jewellery

Benjamin Lignel
Io ce l'ho d'oro (Yeah...but mine is gold), 2007
H 21 × W 11 × D 24 cm
Fine gold, stuffed pigeon
Photo: Enrico Bartolucci, Paris

'*Io ce l'ho d'oro*: an experiment on the ambivalent use of accessories to mock or ape the demeanour of our betters. The piece is about both body extension and carnival: the fact that I used a pigeon for a model should not obscure the fact that this is – as all art always is – about us.'

Benjamin Lignel

Wendy Ramshaw CBE RDI
Blue Knight, 2009
Complex set of rings, 18 carat white and yellow gold on a blue anodised aluminium stand.
Photo: Graham Pym

'*Blue Knight* is both a sculptural object and a collection of rings. The title of the piece refers to the game of chess. Shapes made from 18 carat yellow and white gold gripped together in the centre appear to be armorial in form and character. They spread in a defensive manner around the blue body of the whole piece.

'In any game there are participants. Here the participant is the owner of the set of rings which can be worn on their hand in many different ways. The game is to learn all the possible combinations and meet the objective by discovering choices for everyday ease of wearing and the challenge of arranging a sculptural event upon their hand.'

Wendy Ramshaw CBE RDI

Marsden Woo Gallery is internationally recognised for showing innovative work from leading artists across the field of applied arts.

A continuous programme of solo or small group exhibitions runs in the ground floor gallery, featuring new work from the stable of gallery artists which has just grown to include three talented newcomers. Occasional collaborations bring in invited artists and smaller more spontaneous exhibitions are held in the new downstairs Project Space.

Our collections of key works, both contemporary and from the recent past, can be seen and handled by appointment in our basement space.

Staff
Tatjana Marsden
Nelson Woo
Alida Sayer

Contact
17–18 Great Sutton Street
London
EC1V 0DN UK
T +44(0)207 336 6396
E info@marsdenwoo.com
www.marsdenwoo.com

Artists represented
Gordon Baldwin
Alison Britton
Caroline Broadhead
Ken Eastman
Philip Eglin
Kerry Jameson
Maria Van Kesteren
Chun Liao
Robert Marsden
Nao Matsunaga
Carol McNicoll
Sara Radstone
Nicholas Rena
Michael Rowe
Martin Smith
Emma Woffenden
Dawn Youll

Gordon Baldwin
Vessel (*Klee Cloud 11*), 2009
H 26 × W 41 × D 32 cm
Ceramic
Photo: Philip Sayer

Emma Woffenden
I Call Her, Mother, 2010
H 130 × W 50 × D 70 cm
Glass, mixed media and found object
Photo: Philip Sayer

Established by the Crafts Council of Ireland in 2000, the National Craft Gallery exhibits a programme of ground-breaking national and international contemporary craft.

Staff

Úna Parsons, Chief Executive
Brian McGee, Head of Market Development
Ann Mulrooney, Curator and Exhibitions Manager
Des Doyle, Collector Programme and Craft Tourism Development Manager

Contact

Castle Yard
Kilkenny
Ireland
T +353(0)56 7796147
F +353(0)56 7763754
E ncg@ccoi.ie
www.nationalcraftgallery.ie

Artists represented

Sara Flynn, ceramic
Joe Hogan, basketmaking
Frances Lambe, ceramic
John Lee, furniture
Nest Design, furniture
Nuala O'Donovan, ceramic
Cóilín Ó Dubhghaill, metal
Mandy Parslow, ceramic

Nuala O'Donovan

Coral, Addition-Division, 2009
H 24 × W 39 × D 24 cm
High-fired unglazed porcelain
Photo: Rory Moore

O'Donovan creates complex sculptural forms in unglazed porcelain, drawn from patterns of growth and repetition in nature. This work is informed by research into the origins and history of pattern, the occurrence of geometry in nature, and the principles of irregular forms, such as fractals. The resulting works are delicate, accretive constructions in varying and multiple proportions, hand-built over long periods of time.

Cóilín Ó Dubhghaill

Softstack, *Closed Segment*, 2008
Softstack: H 25 × W 13 × D 13 cm
Closed Segment: H 20 × W 22 × D 22 cm
Patinated copper
Photo: Rory Moore

Ó Dubhghaill explores vessel forms in his work, focusing on the ways in which material processes can create both the form and surface of a piece. This is driven by his current research into hand-made alloys and patination techniques, a continuation of his doctorate studies at Tokyo University of Fine Arts, Japan. Ó Dubhghaill's work breaks new ground in exploring the interplay of modern construction methods with traditional Japanese patination techniques.

Rosemarie Jäger attaches equal importance to fine and applied art. Her constant criterion is to present individual art objects of unique quality.

Staff

Rosemarie Jäger
Anna Pirk

Contact

65239 Hochheim am Main (Frankfurt)
Germany
T + 49(0)6146 2203
F + 49(0)6146 601068
E galerie-r.jaeger@t-online.de
www.rosemarie-jaeger.de

Artists represented

Otto Baier, metal
Kerstin Becker, metal
Rudolf Bott, metal
Paul Derrez, metal
Bettina Dittlmann, jewellery
Katja Hoeltermann, metal
Kap-Sun Hwang, ceramic
Michael Jank, jewellery
Ike Jünger, jewellery
Kati Jünger, ceramic
Bohyung Koh, metal
Beate Kuhn, ceramic
Young-Jae Lee, ceramic
Beate Leonards, metal
Adam Löffler, wood
Christa Lühtje, jewellery
Josephine Lützel, metal
Sebastian Scheid, ceramic
Ja-Kyung Shin, metal
Ursula Ullmann, glass
Peter Verburg, metal
Jan Wege, metal
Gotlind Weigel, ceramic
Chikako Yoshikawa, ceramic
Masamichi Yoshikawa, ceramic
Annamaria Zanella, jewellery
Annette Zey, metal

Bettina Dittlmann

Brooch, yellow, untitled, 2008
H 5.6 × W 5 × D 4 cm
Iron, enamel
Photo: Michael Jank

'Red red red red red red red and yellow. I try to work with the enamel, try to understand its laws and try to break them. But the enamel always wins!'

Bettina Dittlmann

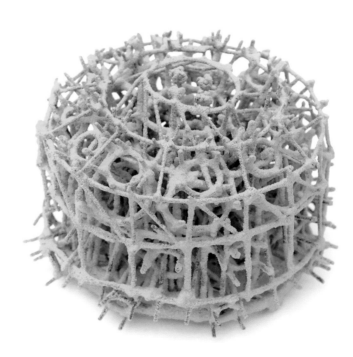

Kap-Sun Hwang
Beaker, 2009
H 24 × W 9.5 cm
Porcelain
Photo: Kap-Sun Hwang

'With ten fingers and two palms, we can easily form a small and simple vessel. My piece, composed of many different parts, with the interior treated with glaze and the exterior finely polished, brings ...to mind a bird's egg.'

Kap-Sun Hwang

The Galleries at Ruthin Craft Centre are the premier space in Wales for generating monograph and survey exhibitions by the very best contemporary applied artists from both Wales and beyond.

Staff

Philip Hughes, Gallery Director
Jane Gerrard, Deputy Director

Contact

Park Road
Ruthin
Denbighshire
LL15 1BB UK
T +44(0)1824 704774
F +44(0)1824 702060
E thegallery@rccentre.org.uk
www.ruthincraftcentre.org.uk

Artists represented

Kevin Coates, jewellery
Claire Curneen, ceramic
Rozanne Hawksley, textile
Catrin Howell, ceramic
Walter Keeler, ceramic
Pamela Rawnsley, metal
Audrey Walker, textile

Walter Keeler

Ribbed stem teapot, *Cut-branch*, 2008
H 28 cm
Whieldon ware
Photo: Dewi Tannatt Lloyd

Function is a central issue in every pot that Walter Keeler makes, rising to the challenge of utilitarian demands he experiences a timeless pleasure in useful objects. Making playful reference to the eccentric inventiveness of the emerging pottery industry in 18th-century Staffordshire, thorns and branches which seem daunting, even threatening, are turned to practical ends as thumb holds on handles. This is not just a teapot, it is an artefact with rich meaning.

Claire Curneen

St Sebastian, 2008
H 46 cm
Porcelain
Photo: Dewi Tannatt Lloyd

'Claire Curneen's poignant figures assuredly command their spaces with their otherworldly messages of quiet selflessness and self-denial, and intense portrayals of sacrifice, and the dying agonies of the saints. These figures encompass eternal and fundamental facets of all human experience: love, loss, suffering and compassion. Yet they always embody hope. They offer us temporary respite from the preoccupations of every-day life, an opportunity for reflection, and a chance to appreciate the work of one of the most expressive ceramic sculptors working in Europe today.'

Fennah Podschies, 2008

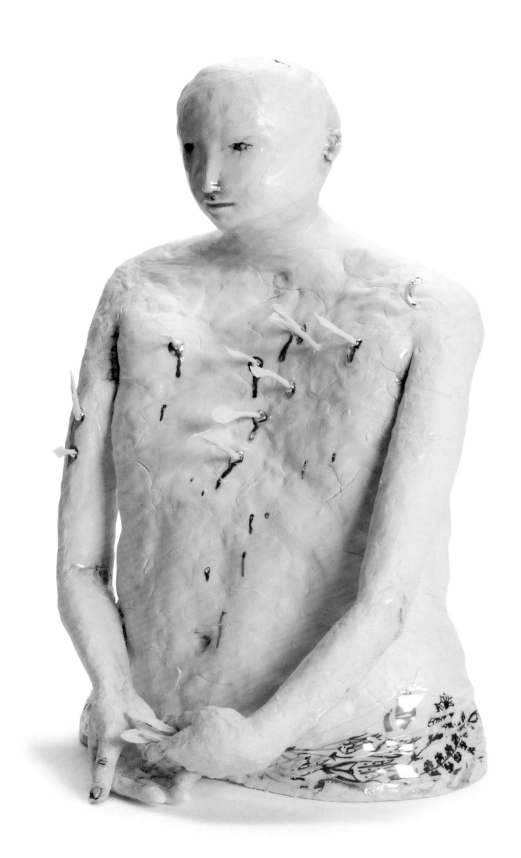

Kevin Coates
Mounted pin brooch, *Lunar Hare*, 2007
H 3 × W 2.8 cm (without pin)
20 carat gold, black mother-of-pearl, yellow
sapphire, silver, 18 carat white gold pin
Mount: mixed media
Photo: Clarissa Bruce

'Kevin Coates creates visual poetry...
For Coates, there are always mysteries,
tiny or vast, to be marvelled at and explored,
and his joy comes from the making of
connections – between objects and people,
myths and symbols, nature and artefact,
philosophy and music, words and
materials... With an alchemist's skill, he
can transform the apparently mundane
into the indisputably magical... These pins,
small in scale but rich in meaning, each
one resting happily within the "comfortable
bed" of its own notebook page.'

Dr Elizabeth Goring, A Notebook of Pins, 2009

Rozanne Hawksley
Pale Rider, 2008
H 38 × W 22 cm
Textile, lace, bone, leather, found objects
Photo: Dewi Tannatt Lloyd

'The reality and informality of the gloves
in Rozanne Hawksley's sculpture, their
tints and textured softness, allows them to
serve as perfect analogues for real human
hands, emphasising human variety, human
corporeality and human touch, in a never-
ending cycle of comfort... Attempting
subsequently to analyse why her work
had affected me so deeply, I puzzled over
how it was that the effect continued long
afterwards in memory. What caught me
unawares was its gentle mix of wit and
sorrow, beauty and sadness, tenderness
and mischief.'

Dr Ruth Richardson,
For *Rozanne Hawksley*, 2009

Sarah Myerscough Fine Art will be exhibiting museum-quality turned and carved wood by internationally renowned artists from America, Australia and Europe.

Staff

Sarah Myerscough
Andy Stewart
Freya Smaill

Contact

15–16 Brooks Mews
Mayfair
London
W1K 4DS UK
T +44(0)20 7495 0069
E info@sarahmyerscough.com
www.sarahmyerscough.com

Artists represented

Christian Burchard
Liam Flynn
Mark Hanvey
John Jordan
Bud Latven
Malcolm Martin and Gaynor Dowling
Philip Moulthrop
Marc Ricourt
Grant Vaughan

Christian Burchard

Family Affair, 2009
Bleached Madrone Burl
Various sizes
Photo: Christian Burchard

Burchard was born in Germany and originally studied furniture making, which developed into sculptural turned wood pieces because of the creative freedom the practice offered. His preferred material is Pacific Madrone Burl, a wood that changes as it dries, finding its own form. Collections of Burchard's work can be found in the Museum of Art and Design, New York, Detroit Art Museum and Museum for Contemporary Art, Honolulu, Hawaii.

Grant Vaughan
Enfolded Form #1
Australian White Beech, 2009
H 60 cm, Diam. 30 cm

Vaughan was born in Gunnedah, Australia
in 1954, and his beautiful and organic
turned wood work still exudes a strong
relationship with the land, an influence
made manifest in his use of the stunning
locally sourced wood.

Grant has exhibited throughout Australia,
and since the late 90s has gained
international recognition through exhibitions in the US, Far East and Europe.
He is represented in many international
private and public collections, including
the Museum of Fine Arts, Boston, Cincinatti
Art Museum and the National Gallery of
Australia, Canberra.

Terra Delft Gallery, founded in 1986, is a gallery for contemporary ceramics. In addition to exhibitions featuring both Dutch and foreign ceramists, the gallery also serves as a permanent sales point. The collection ranges from applied art to autonomous pieces.

Staff

Joka Doedens
Simone Haak
Etty Walda

Contact

Nieuwstraat 7
Delft
The Netherlands
NL–2611 HK
T +31(0)15 2147072
F +31(0)15 2147072
E info@terra-delft.nl
www.terra-delft.nl

Artists represented

Louise Hindsgavl
Márta Nagy
Mariëtte van der Ven
Pauline Wiertz
Henk Wolvers

Márta Nagy
Desire, 2009
H 35.5 × W 18.5 × D 17 cm
Porcelain, stoneware
Photo: István Füzi

Nagy works with themes and symbols. Her objects are characterised by the diversity of her forms and decoration. Her work is hand built using snow-white Hungarian porcelain and red-firing chamotte clay, almost always combining the two. The techniques she uses to colour her works are various: metal oxide, coloured clay, lustre glaze, gold and silver leaf. The combination of these exceptional colourings are her signature.

Mariëtte van der Ven
Burden, 2008
H 70 × W 25 × D 25 cm
Porcelain, textile, leather, wood

Diversity and the human form are the
theme for van der Ven's sculpture. She
does not attempt to depict the beautiful
aspects of people in her work, but rather
the less attractive or pleasing aspects.
Her works express the relationship of art
and reality. Her starting point is always
the figure. Her alterations of reality are
calculated to make the viewer conscious
of the absurdity of the seemingly normal.
The combination of monochrome ceramic
with materials such as cloth and leather
are poetic and softened, creating space
for personal reflection.

The Scottish Gallery, established in 1842, specialises in Scottish, UK and international contemporary objects, ceramics, glass, furniture, jewellery, metalwork, textiles and sculpture. It holds significant solo and group exhibitions throughout the year.

Staff

Christina Jansen, Director
Rupert Johnstone
Bryony Windsor

Contact

16 Dundas Street
Edinburgh
EH3 6HZ UK
T +44(0)131 558 1200
F +44(0)131 558 3900
E mail@scottish-gallery.co.uk
www.scottish-gallery.co.uk

Artists represented

Malcolm Appleby, jewellery/metal
Peter Chang, jewellery
Katharine Coleman, glass
Jack Cunningham, jewellery
Ken Eastman, ceramic
Sally Fawkes, glass
Robert Foster, metal
Anna Gordon, jewellery
Dorothy Hogg, jewellery
Takahiro Kondo, ceramic
William Lee, metal
Jacqueline Lillie, jewellery
Bodil Manz, ceramic
Dante Marioni, glass
Grant McCaig, metal
Alison McConachie, glass
Jim Partridge and Liz Walmsley, wood
David Poston, jewellery
David Pottinger, ceramic
Frances Priest, ceramic
Wendy Ramshaw, jewellery
Merete Rasmussen, ceramic
Jasmin Rowlandson, ceramic
Jacqueline Ryan, jewellery
Julian Stair, ceramic

Jacqueline Lillie

Neckpiece, *Orange Grey neckpiece*, 2009
Rope, Corian®
H 17 × W 14 cm

'Jewellery is a reflection of one's attitudes towards life and one's surroundings. At the same time, the pieces should draw on the traditions of the past and take them a step further. The ultimate test with any piece of art is the impact that the piece has on the person looking at it, or in my case on the person wearing it. My work is very much a labour of love in which I have tried to meet the client's urge for self-adornment and satisfy my own desire for poetry and elegance.'

Jacqueline Lillie

Bodil Manz

Hommage a Vilhelm Lundstrøm, 2009
Eggshell porcelain
H 15 cm, Diam. 18/12 cm
Photo: Brahl Fotografi

Manz was born in Copenhagen in 1943
and studied ceramics at the School of Arts
& Craft in Copenhagen. She established
a studio with her late husband, ceramist
Richard Manz, in 1967 in Horve, where
she continues to live and work today.

Manz has been known as a master
of eggshell porcelain for many years now.
The Scottish Gallery will be exhibiting her
signature, near paper-thin cast porcelain
cylinders alongside her architectural
three dimensional forms. In 2008 she
was honoured with a major retrospective
exhibition at the Kunstindustrimuseet in
Copenhagen. She is represented in many
public collections including the Musée des
Arts Décoratifs, The Louvre, Paris and the
Victoria & Albert Museum, London.

Situated in the heart of Tokyo, Yufuku represents Japanese and international artists whose works define space itself. Focusing on ceramics, metal and glass, Yufuku's artists, wielding traditional techniques enhanced by triumphs in both innovation and imagination, push the boundaries of their media to brave new heights.

Staff

Tom M. Aoyama, Gallery Owner
Maki Yamashita, Gallery Representative
Wahei Aoyama, International Director and Chief Curator

Contact

Annecy Aoyama 1st Floor
2–6–12 Minami-Aoyama
Minato-ku, Tokyo
Japan 107–0062
T +81(3)5411 2900
F +81(3)5411 2901
E wahei@yufuku.net
www.yufuku.net

Artists represented

Sueharu Fukami, ceramic
Masahiko Ichino, ceramic
Niyoko Ikuta, glass
Akihiro Maeta, ceramic
Ken Mihara, ceramic
Shigekazu Nagae, ceramic
Ryota Nishikata, metal
Gaku Shakunaga, ceramic
Rikie Shojiguchi, glass
Atsushi Takagaki, ceramic
Naoki Takeyama, cloisonné
Takahiro Yede, metal
Byong-Uk Yeo, ceramic
Yukio Yoshita, ceramic

Atsushi Takagaki

Akane Seiji Kosoku (*Celadon with Scarlet Hues: Binding Light*), 2009
H 52 × W 36.5 × D 33 cm
Stoneware, multiple celadon glazes
Photo: Gakuji Tanaka

'Developed in ancient times, celadon arrived as the materialisation of an ideal, and remains a style that requires great perseverance. Celadon glazes are rich, its serene blues highly praised. Creating harmony within the crackled glaze is difficult, and ceramists are hampered by the weight of history. Though I maintain celadon's highest standards, as I search for new contemporary forms, I have invented a new celadon style called *Akane Seiji* (celadon with scarlet hues).'

Atsushi Takagaki

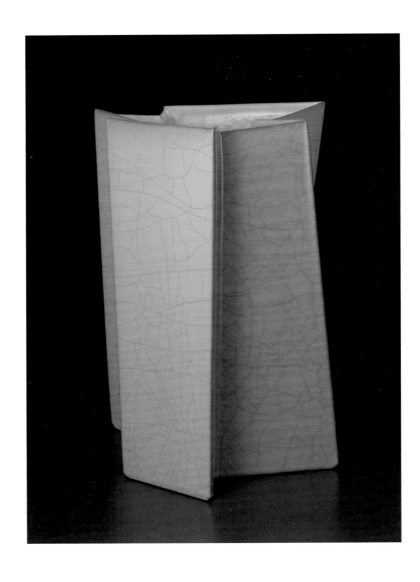

'Using fragments of laminated sheet
glass, I draw lines in space. A viewer's
impression of this work changes
dramatically with the slightest change
in viewing-angle and light. Ultimately,
I believe the image that impresses itself
on the viewer's heart represents the
true and final nature of my work.'

Niyoko Ikuta

PHILLIPS

de PURY & COMPANY

DESIGN

IMPORTANT WORKS BY HANS COPER AND LUCIE RIE

AUCTION 5 JUNE 2010 **NEW YORK**
Viewing 29 May – 5 June

Phillips de Pury & Company 450 West 15 Street New York 10011
Enquiries Ben Williams +44 20 7318 4027 / +1 212 940 1268 bwilliams@phillipsdepury.com
Catalogues +44 20 7318 4039 / +1 212 940 1240
www.phillipsdepury.com

CRAFTS

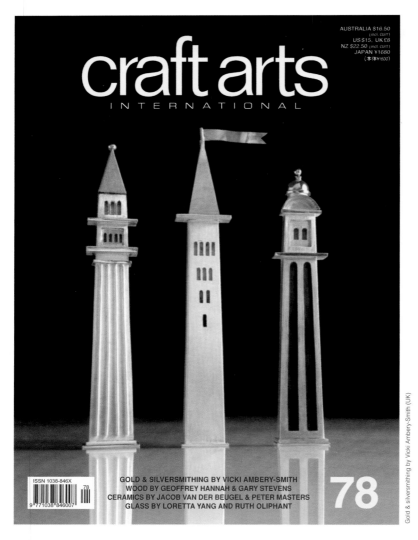

AUSTRALIA $16.50 (incl. GST)
US $15, UK £8
NZ $22.50 (incl. GST)
JAPAN ¥1680
(本体¥1600)

craft arts
I N T E R N A T I O N A L

ISSN 1038-846X

GOLD & SILVERSMITHING BY VICKI AMBERY-SMITH
WOOD BY GEOFFREY HANNAH & GARY STEVENS
CERAMICS BY JACOB VAN DER BEUGEL & PETER MASTERS
GLASS BY LORETTA YANG AND RUTH OLIPHANT

78

Gold & silversmithing by Vicki Ambery-Smith (UK)

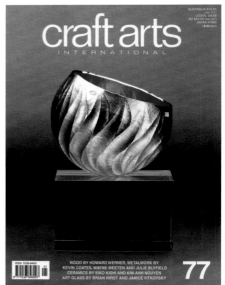

AUSTRALIA $16.50
US $15, UK £8
NZ $22.50 (incl. GST)
JAPAN ¥1680
(本体¥1600)

craft arts
I N T E R N A T I O N A L

ISSN 1038-846X

WOOD BY HOWARD WERNER, METALWORK BY
KEVIN COATES, WAYNE MEETEN AND JULIE BLYFIELD
CERAMICS BY EIKO KISHI AND KIM-ANH NGUYEN
ART GLASS BY BRIAN HIRST AND JANICE VITKOVSKY

77

Britannia silver by Wayne Meeten (UK)

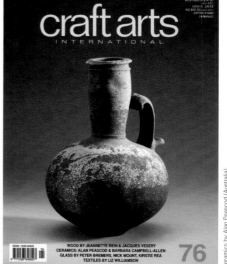

AUSTRALIA $16.50 (incl. GST)
US $15, UK £8
NZ $22.50 (incl. GST)
JAPAN ¥1680
(本体¥1600)

craft arts
I N T E R N A T I O N A L

ISSN 1038-846X

WOOD BY JEANNETTE REIN & JACQUES VESERY
CERAMICS: ALAN PEASCOD & BARBARA CAMPBELL-ALLEN
GLASS BY PETER BREMERS, NICK MOUNT, KIRSTIE REA
TEXTILES BY LIZ WILLIAMSON

76

Ceramics by Alan Peascod (Australia)

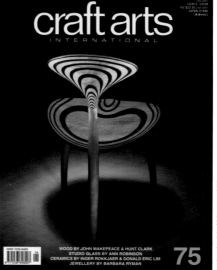

AUSTRALIA $16.50 (incl. GST)
US $15, UK £8
NZ $22.50 (incl. GST)
JAPAN ¥1680
(本体¥1600)

craft arts
I N T E R N A T I O N A L

ISSN 1038-846X

WOOD BY JOHN MAKEPEACE & HUNT CLARK
STUDIO GLASS BY ANN ROBINSON
CERAMICS BY INGER ROKKJAER & DONALD ERIC LIM
JEWELLERY BY BARBARA RYMAN

75

Furniture by John Makepeace (UK)

Documenting the latest in contemporary
Visual and Applied Arts

THIS well-established independent journal is devoted to the documentation of contemporary craftwork and "new art forms" that come within the broad fields of the visual and applied arts. But it is not limited by these classifications and crosses traditional boundaries in the pursuit and exploration of innovative concepts and standards of excellence that challenge conventional aesthetic experience and enrich the quality of life.

Each issue of *Craft Arts International* contains 128 pages in full colour, with over 400 illustrations of innovative concepts and new work by leading artists and designer/makers, supported by authoritative and comprehensive texts that offer vital and stimulating reading for anyone interested in the contemporary visual and applied arts.

Craft Arts International
PO Box 363, Neutral Bay, Sydney, NSW 2089, Australia
Tel: +61-2 9908 4797, Fax: +61-2 9953 1576
Website: www.craftarts.com.au
Subscriptions: subs@craftarts.com.au Advertising: info@craftarts.com.au

2010 British Glass Biennale

The UK's major exhibition of contemporary glass

27 August – 11 September
Open daily 10 – 5
Ruskin Glass Centre
Stourbridge, UK
www.biennale.org.uk

Angela Jarman, Geode, 2009
Photo Credit: Alan Tabor

LOTTERY FUNDED

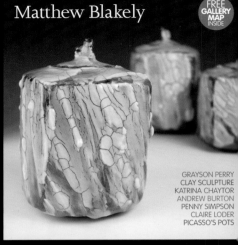

SOFA
WEST
SANTA FE

Sculpture Objects & Functional Art Fair

July 8-11, 2010
Santa Fe Convention Center

Opening Night Wednesday, July 7
Special Member Preview for Museum of New Mexico Foundation

SAVE THE DATE
SOFA CHICAGO – November 5-7, 2010

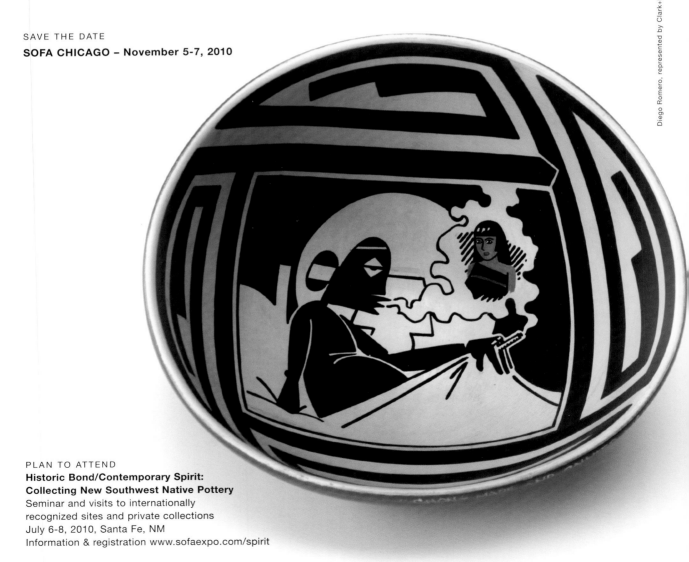

Diego Romero, represented by Clark+DelVecchio

PLAN TO ATTEND
Historic Bond/Contemporary Spirit:
Collecting New Southwest Native Pottery
Seminar and visits to internationally
recognized sites and private collections
July 6-8, 2010, Santa Fe, NM
Information & registration www.sofaexpo.com/spirit

sofaexpo.com

Produced by The Art Fair Company, Inc.

CHROME YELLOW BOOKS

SPECIALISTS IN CONTEMPORARY
EUROPEAN ART AND CRAFT PUBLICATIONS

THE BOOKSHOP AT COLLECT WILL
FEATURE THE BOOKS AND CATALOGUES
OF EXHIBITING ARTISTS ALONGSIDE
A COMPREHENSIVE SELECTION OF
ART AND CRAFT PUBLICATIONS

BOOKSTANDS AT CRAFT EVENTS,
FESTIVALS, CONFERENCES, SYMPOSIUMS

SUPPLIERS TO UNIVERSITY LIBRARIES,
MUSEUMS AND GALLERIES

SONIA COLLINS
T +44 (0)1787 281112
E SONIAANDMICHAEL@AOL.COM
WWW.CHROMEYELLOWBOOKS.COM